Short is good

This is me with Asher.
He is a lot shorter than me.

Asher is shorter than the rest of my pals, too. He feels a bit sad.

His mum and dad think
he is just right as he is.

His big sister tells him, "You can fit into tight spots and have lots of leg room in the car!"

You can fit in your bed! My feet hang off the end of my bed.

I go with Asher and his mum
to the shops. Asher gets a
pair of joggers. But they are
too long for his legs.

9

At tennis, Asher hits harder
than me. The coach tells me,
"Asher is short, but he is strong."

Asher is a better runner than me. I tell him, "My legs are longer, but you are much quicker."

As we run, Asher spots a short cut. He tells me, "It is quicker if we cross this paddock."

We get to a wooden railing.
It is hard for me to go under.

But it is no problem for Asher.
He slips under the railing.

I jump the railing. My shorts
split and I land in the mud!

Asher grins. "Perhaps it's not that bad to be short. It might just be better!"

Words to blend

short	railing	than
right	think	tight
room	feet	hang
shops	pair	long
wooden	good	hard
shorts	might	for
too		

Before reading

Synopsis: Asher is shorter than his pals. His mum even has to take up his trousers. But Asher is a good tennis player and a fast runner.

Review phoneme/s: ar or ur ow oi ear air ure

New phoneme: er

Story discussion: Look at the cover, and read the title together. Ask: *Who do you recognise on the cover? Is Sam taller or shorter than the other boy? What do you think about the title? Is it sometimes good to be short?* Share ideas about what might happen in the story.

Link to prior learning: Display the digraph *er*. Remind children that digraphs are two letters that make one sound together. Explain that *er* can come in the middle of a word (like *perhaps*) or at the end (like *summer*). Display *perhaps* and *summer* and practise reading them together.

Vocabulary check: Railing – a sort of fence or barrier. Turn to page 14, and ask children to find the word *railing* and point to the picture of it.

Decoding practice: Turn to page 16 and ask children to find as many words with *er* as they can on this page. Write the words they find (*Asher, perhaps, better*) and ask children to add dots under the single-letter graphemes and dashes under the digraphs. Then sound out and blend the words.

Tricky word practice: Display the words *me* and *we*. Ask: *What do these words have in common?* Children can underline the tricky part (*e*, which makes the sound /ee/) and practise reading and writing these words.

After reading

Apply learning: Discuss the story. Ask: *How does Asher feel about his height at the end of the story? Do you think he's right that being short could be better than being tall?* Talk about the fact that it doesn't really matter how tall people are – what they do and how they behave towards others is far more important.

Comprehension

- What problem does Asher have when he goes to buy joggers?

- Asher is better than Sam at some things. Can you name one?

- What is one good thing about being short, according to the story?

Fluency

- Pick a page that most of the group read quite easily. Ask them to reread it with pace and expression. Model how to do this if necessary.

- Turn to page 16, and ask children to read the words Asher says. Can they read with lots of expression so that it sounds as if he's really talking?

- Practise reading the words on page 17.

Tricky words review

me	we	my
as	you	are
was	said	have
your	they	there
to	be	go